CiTV

Telly Tots

CiTV

Hi, I'm Danielle ...**and I'm Stephen**

Hello from the first CiTV Telly Tots Annual. If you're a reader of our magazine, you'll know these pages are full of sunny stories and activities, starring all your favourite characters.

If you are a new reader, then it's lovely to welcome you. We hope you'll have lots of fun.

I'm Tom ...**and I'm Andrea**

A note to Grown-up Telly Tots

We hope that you find plenty in CiTV Telly Tots Annual to entertain and stimulate young minds. Your help and involvement makes all the difference to encourage confidence and an inquisitive nature.

At first your child may just enjoy looking at the pictures and talking about them. However, here are a few suggestions to get the most from these pages...

★ Go at your child's own pace.

★ Offer lots of praise.

★ Point to the page numbers and say them out loud.

★ Point to and count the objects in the pictures (which also helps to develop observational skills).

● EDITOR Deborah Tate ● DESIGN Ian Melville, Charles Wrigley, Caroline Potts ● PICTURE/TEXT STORY WRITER Lew Stringer ● PRODUCT MANAGER Peter Hey ● COVER LOGO Steve Cook, Dave Hickman ● MANAGING DIRECTOR Rob McMenemy.

What's in Telly Tots

Annual 2001

1

Mopatop was waiting to see who his first customer of the day would be. Everyone loved to visit Mopatop's Shop.

2

"Ding!" went the bell above the doorway. Mopatop opened the door and looked out. "Here comes a customer now," he said.

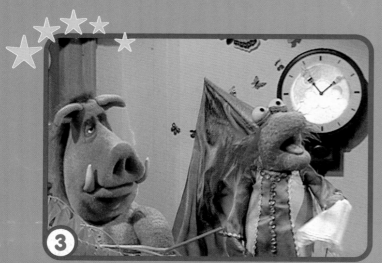

3

It was Princess Lulabelle. "Can you help me, Mopatop?" she asked. "My handsome Frog Prince has turned into a hog!"

4

"I'm looking for a kiss that will turn a hog into a frog," said the princess. "I'm sure we have one in stock," said Mopatop.

Mopatop was very proud of his shop. It had everything you could ever dream of and Mopatop always greeted each customer with a smile.

5

Up popped Mopatop's assistant, Puppyduck. "Anything I can do to help you?" she asked the princess.

6

"Please go down to the Kisses Department, Puppyduck," said Mopatop, "and find a kiss that can turn a hog into a frog."

7

Puppyduck found what she was looking for. The princess tried the kiss to turn a hog into a frog. "Here goes," she said.

8

"Oh no!" cried Princess Lulabelle. "The kiss hasn't turned the hog into a frog. It's turned him into a dog!" What had gone wrong?

9 "I must have given Princess Lulabelle the Hog-into-Dog Kiss instead of the Hog-into-Frog Kiss by mistake," said Puppyduck.

10 "Don't worry, Puppyduck," said Mopatop. "Just find a Dog-into-Frog Kiss instead." But Puppyduck couldn't find one.

11 "We're out of Dog-into-Frog Kisses," said Puppyduck. "Keep looking," said Mopatop. "I'm sure you'll find one."

12 Puppyduck returned to the Kisses Department and looked again. "Aha!" she said after a while. "I've found one!"

"Quick!" said Princess Lulabelle, "Let me try it out." The princess gave the dog a big, sloppy kiss. "Mmmwahh!"

Straight away, the dog changed into the Frog Prince. "Hooray! Hooray! It worked," said the happy princess.

"There you go," said Mopatop, smiling, "if you look hard enough, you always find what you want in the end."

the end

WHAT CAN YOU REMEMBER?

1 What was the name of the princess?

2 Which department did Puppy-duck go to?

3 What happened when the princess kissed the hog?

4 Which kiss worked in the end?

Answers: 1: Lulabelle. 2: The Kisses Department. 3: It turned into a dog. 4: The Dog-into-Frog Kiss.

True footprints?

Dog and Duck

Have you ever wondered what Dog's pawprints would look like if he wasn't on wheels? Can you guess the shape of Duck's footmarks too?

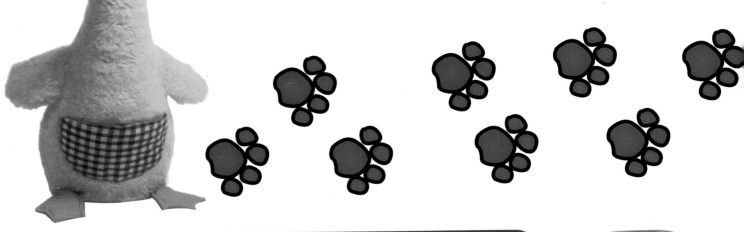

'Quack' if you think that the above footprints belong to Duck.

'Bark' if you think that these are Dog's pawprints.

If you 'Quacked' or 'Barked', then you guessed wrong! Duck has webbed feet like the footmarks shown in orange. Dog would have pawprints, like the ones shown in blue.

Win a set of CiTV Favourites Videos

We have 30 sets of CiTV Favourites videos to give away, thanks to Contender Entertainment Group. That's more than 2 hours of superb CiTV entertainment!

HOW TO ENTER

Just fill in the missing word of the following CiTV favourite:

Mopatop's ....

Write the answer on a postcard or sealed empty envelope. Add your name, address, and age, and post it before the closing date of 27 January 2001 to:-

CiTV Favourites Video Competition, CiTV Annual, Egmont World Ltd., Deanway Technology Centre, Wilmslow Road, Handforth, Cheshire, SK9 3FB.

Rules:-

30 winners will be chosen at random and notified by post. The judges' decision will be final. No correspondence will be entered into. The winners' names will be made available from Egmont World Ltd., (on request) after 5 February 2001. Please enclose a stamped addressed envelope. Employees (and their relatives) of Egmont World Ltd., and their associated companies are not eligible to enter. Entries are limited to one per person. Competition is open to residents of the UK, Channel Isles and Ireland. The Publishers reserve the right to vary prizes, subject to availability. Closing date for entries is 27 January 2001.

Tommy the Bat

1

In an old country barn,
lived Tommy the Bat.
He lived with his friend,
young Rita the Rat.

2

Rita and Tommy
like playing at night.
For a rat and a bat
tend to sleep when it's light.

3

"That's that for tonight,"
young Rita said.
"Dawn has arrived.
It's time for our bed."

4

Rita lay down
on a bundle of straw.
And before very long,
she started to snore.

Tommy the Bat finds that sleep just won't come, until he receives some help from his Mum.

5

Tommy curled up
in a tight little heap.
But something was wrong -
he just couldn't sleep.

6

He couldn't get comfy.
Tom said, "I can't sleep!"
So Rita replied,
"Try counting some sheep."

7

He counted aloud -
to a thousand and four.
Until Rita cried out,
"Please, don't count anymore!"

8

"Perhaps you're not tired,"
a little mouse said.
"Do lots of flying,
and then go to bed."

9

With a 'Whizz' and a 'Vroom'
Tommy flew round and round.
But he still couldn't sleep
when he lay on the ground.

10

Said a wise old Barn Owl,
"My plan never fails.
I have a big book
of fun, night-time tales."

11

The owl was quite right -
sleep came as she read.
But not to poor Tommy -
the owl slept instead!

12

Tom called for his Mother,
and started to weep.
"I've tried lots of ways,
but I can't get to sleep!"

13

"Well, didn't you know?"
Mum said with a frown,
"That bats only sleep
when they hang upside-down?"

14

ZZZZ

So he hung upside-down,
by the tips of his toes.
And then at long last,
Tommy started to doze.

WHAT CAN YOU REMEMBER?

1 Where does Tommy live?

2 Who does Tommy live with?

3 Who fell asleep reading a book?

4 Who's idea helped Tommy get to sleep?

5 Can you think of a word that rhymes with bat and rat?

Answers: 1: In a barn. 2: Rita the Rat. 3: The barn Owl. 4: Tommy's Mother. 5: Cat, mat, etc.

Watch Animal Stories
To have a good time
Then try to make up
Your own little rhyme

the end

Name the Animals

Can you help Captain Pugwash by naming the different animals he has to catch.

Captain Pugwash is taking a group of animals to the zoo in Montebuffo, but they have escaped and are running wild all over the ship.

THE ADVENTURES OF
Captain Pugwash ™

Yell SHIVERING SHARKS! as loud as you can if you spotted these animals:-
1. Parrot or Bird. 2. Monkey. 3. Dog. 4. Camel. 6. Sheep.

The helpful weather

1

Whenever the house is empty, Dog and Duck come to life. The two toys are the best of friends, and love to explore.

2

"I wonder what we can do today?" said Duck. "It looks like it might rain," replied Dog, "so perhaps we should stay indoors."

3

"Let's explore the attic," said Dog. "There's old and interesting things up there." Duck thought this was a good idea.

4

The attic was dark and full of old items the family didn't use any more. "It's a bit dusty and creepy, but I like it," said Dog.

Dog and Duck are no ordinary toys. Together with their friends, Elephant, Piano and Tele they come to life when their owners' backs are turned.

Dog and Duck

5

Suddenly, the room was lit up by a flash of lightning. "Oooh!" shouted Dog and Duck. They didn't like thunderstorms.

6

"The weather is always changing," said Duck. "It was sunny yesterday". "Why can't it be sunny everyday?" Dog asked.

7

"Very good question," replied Duck. "Let's ask Tele. She will know, because Tele knows everything."

8

Dog and Duck went downstairs to the kitchen to ask Tele. "The weather changes to help nature," said Tele. "How?" asked Duck.

9

"Let me show you a cartoon to explain," said Tele. Her screen began to show pictures of a rain cloud, the wind, and the sun.

10

"We need the warmth from the sun to help things grow," said Tele, "but wind and rain are useful too."

11

"It's horrible to get wet in a rainstorm," said Tele, "but the plants and flowers need the water to feed them so they can grow."

12

"And the wind scatters the seeds from plants and flowers so that more of them can grow," explained Tele.

"We understand," said Duck. "The weather looks after nature." They looked towards the window. "Look at that!" said Dog.

The rain had stopped, and there was a colourful rainbow in the sky. "That's so pretty," said Duck. "Amazing!" gasped Dog.

"The changing weather will always gives us both something to talk about," said Duck. Dog agreed.

the end

Piano Puzzle

1 Find 5 differences between these pictures and say them out loud.

2 What musical instrument is Teddy playing?

Can you answer these questions about Annie and Teddy's sing-a-long.

3 What does Annie have in her hand?

4 What is Teddy sitting on?

5 What is Annie wearing around her neck?

Hum a tune if you got any of these answers right!
1) The candleabra is missing. Teddy's bow is red. Annie has yellow shoes. Annies hair is brown. Teddy's stool is yellow. 2) Piano. 3) A flower or a rose. 4) Stool. 5) Scarf.

MaisieMac's exciting day

1

MaisieMac was going on a day trip to Glasgow with Granny, their neighbour, Mrs McKitty, and her friend Archie.

2

MaisieMac loved to go shopping with Granny. She also enjoyed looking out of the window on the bus.

3

Archie was excited about having a day out too. He helped to pass the time away by munching on a sticky cake.

4

After they arrived, MaisieMac saw a man selling balloons. She bought one each for her and Archie with her pocket money.

aisie MacKenzie is a mischievous kitten who lives with her
ranny in Edinburgh. Her friends call her MaisieMac She loves
o travel just like her daddy, who is a famous explorer.

5

As they walked along, they
spotted a street entertainer.
"Look," giggled MaisieMac.
"Somebody's juggling plastic fish!"

6

Next, they went into a big toy
shop. "Which toy would you like?"
asked Granny. There were so
many to choose from.

7

MaisieMac decided she would like
a book about famous detectives
instead. "This book looks very
exciting," she said.

8

"Look at the time," said Granny.
"We have to catch the train
home." They all had to run, but
they caught the train just in time.

9

Later that evening when they were getting ready for bed, they had an awful shock. "Oh no!" shouted Granny. "We've been burgled!"

10

MaisieMac noticed some footprints leading to the open window. "The burglar must have escaped this way," she said.

11

"There he is!" shouted Archie. The burglar was dazed by the torchlight. "Granny, 'phone the police," said MaisieMac.

12

The burglar tried to run away but the police arrived and caught him. "Hooray!" shouted Granny, "Well done, MaisieMac."

13

"That was very good detective work, MaisieMac," said the policeman. "I learnt it from my new book," replied MaisieMac.

14

The next day, Granny took MaisieMac and Archie to a special tea-shop as a reward for catching the burglar.

15

MaisieMac enjoyed such a special treat. "It's hungry work being a detective," she said. "Toodle-oo the noo!"

the end

WHAT CAN YOU REMEMBER?

1 Which city did Granny take MaisieMac to?

2 What's the name of MaisieMac's friend?

3 What did MaisieMac choose instead of a toy?

4 Who escaped through the window?

Answers: 1: Glasgow. 2: Archie. 3: A book. 4: A burglar.

Mopatop's Shop®

Puppyduck

Colour in this picture, and write your name in the space below.

Mopatop

Coloured in by ....

Buddy's good deed

1

One day, Magic Time Buddy met Hot Rodney at the crossroads. "I'm the fastest in Dream Street," boasted Rodney.

2

Amber and Scarlet, the traffic lights, began to tease Rodney. "We're not ones to gossip, but we've seen much faster Hot Rods than you."

3

To prove them wrong, Hot Rodney zoomed off at top speed. "Stop!" said Buddy. "It's dangerous to drive fast!" But Rodney didn't hear him.

4

Daisy Do-Right, the police car, saw Rodney showing off. She called to the Sleeping Policemen to help. They rolled along, yawning.

Dream Street is a magical place where everyday things come to life. Magic Time Buddy lives and plays here and always comes to the rescue using his special magical powers.

5 "Attention, PC Snooze, PC Snore, and PC Nod Off," said Daisy. "Form a road block, and, hey, let's not be lazy out there."

6 Hot Rodney saw the Sleeping Policemen, but he just turned around and whizzed off in a different direction. Zoom! Zoom!

7 "Rodney isn't really naughty," said Tech, the magic robot, "He just needs to think what he's doing." Buddy wished he could help.

8 Tech knew what to do. He is the Keeper of Magic. "What time is it, Buddy?" he asked. "It's Magic Time!" replied Buddy.

9

"On line and feeling fine," said Tech, as the special magic began to happen and the whole of Dream Street came to life.

10

The magic had changed Buddy. Now he had a magic rope cannon on his back. "Thank you, Tech," said Buddy.

11

"I'm the fastest! I'm the fastest!" laughed Hot Rodney, whizzing past. Buddy fired his magic rope cannon. WHOOSH!

12

The rope cannon hooked onto Rodney's rear bumper, pulling him back. "Hey! I can't move!" said Rodney. "I did it," shouted Buddy.

13

"You could have hurt someone rushing around like that, Rodney," said Daisy. "I realise that now," said Rodney, "I'm sorry."

14

"As for you two," said Daisy, turning to the Gossips, "I want you to do a Do-Right Duty and not gossip about anyone for a week."

15

"You're my hero, Buddy," said Daisy. Amber and Scarlet knew Buddy liked Daisy, but couldn't gossip about them. Well, not for a week anyway!

the end

WHAT CAN YOU REMEMBER?

1 What are the names of the traffic lights?

2 Who was rushing around Dream Street?

3 Who are PC Snooze, PC Snore and PC Nod Off?

4 What did Buddy use to stop Rodney?

Answers: 1. Amber and Scarlet. 2. Hot Rodney. 3. The Sleeping Policemen. 4. A magic rope cannon.

33

MaisieMac's shortbread

YOU WILL NEED:-

* ❀ A bowl
* ❀ A tablespoon
* ❀ A 20cm round tin
* ❀ Greaseproof paper
* ❀ A knife
* ❀ A baking tray
* ❀ Caster sugar

INGREDIENTS:-

* ❀ 75g sugar
* ❀ 150g unsalted butter (at room temperature)
* ❀ 250g flour

Ask a grown-up Telly Tot to help you with this recipe. It's simple, fun, and delicious. Serves eight Tots.

INSTRUCTIONS:-

❁ Preheat oven to 175C/350F gas mark 4.

❁ Rub all the ingredients together in a bowl, until they become crumbly in texture.

❁ Set aside two tablespoons of the mix, and either press the rest into the base of a 20cm round tin, lined with greaseproof paper, or cut into shapes and put on a baking tray.

❁ Sprinkle the reserved mix over the top, and bake for around 25 minutes, until the shortcake is golden and firm to touch. Leave to cool before turning out of the tin.

❁ To serve, sprinkle on caster sugar (if cooked in the tin, cut into eight pieces).

The Treasure Map

THE ADVENTURES OF Captain Pugwash™

1

Captain Pugwash had sent his crew ashore to go shopping in Portobello. He told them that he needed to get on with some important paperwork.

2

Although he really just wanted some peace and quiet to have a little snooze. "It's good being the Captain," he thought.

3

Later, the crew returned to the Black Pig ship. "Did you get your work done, Captain?" asked the Mate. "Er...of course," lied Pugwash.

4

"Did everyone remember to buy food for the ship?" asked Captain Pugwash. "Oh yes," said Willy, and I bought an old Treasure Map!

Can Tom the Cabin boy rescue the blundering pirate, Captain Pugwash, from Cut-throat Jake and his scurvy band of villains?

5

"Soaring seagulls!" exclaimed Captain Pugwash, looking at the map. "This map shows that treasure is buried near here!"

6

That night, they all set out to dig up the treasure. "Spades at the ready, men," said Captain Pugwash. "We'll all be rich by the morning!"

7

Jonah, the Mate, and Willy set to work. "I think we've found something," said the Mate. "Well done, lads," cried Captain Pugwash.

8

Nearby, the nasty pirate Cut-throat Jake was watching. "Aha!" he thought. "I'll have that treasure for myself."

THE BRITT ALLCROFT COMPANY
© Britt Allcroft (Development) Limited 2000.

9

The crew had dug up a small treasure chest. "Let's take it back to the ship," said Captain Pugwash, "and see what treasure is inside."

10

Captain Pugwash and the crew returned to their ship. Cut-throat Jake followed them, determined to steal the treasure.

11

Tom the cabin boy saw Jake trying to climb aboard. "Take that", said Tom, throwing a bucket of water at him.

12

SPLASH! The water soaked the nasty pirate and he fell backwards into the sea. "Bah! I give up," spluttered Jake.

13

"Good work, Tom," said Captain Pugwash. "Now we can open up the treasure chest. I expect it's full of valuable diamonds or gold."

14

But inside the chest was another map, exactly the same as the first one. "We've been fooled," said Tom, "All that digging for nothing!"

15

"Just where did you buy the first map from, Willy?" asked Captain Pugwash. "Um...From a joke shop," said Willy."Oh no!" they all groaned.

the end

WHAT GAN YOU REMEMBER?

1 Who bought the map?

2 Who was the nasty pirate?

3 What did Captain Pugwash hope was in the chest?

4 What was inside the chest?

Answers: 1. Willy. 2. Cut-throat Jake. 3. Diamonds or gold. 4. Another map.

Jolly Video Competition

JAMBOREE™

JAMBOREE™ ANIMALS AND MUSIC FUN! with Floella Benjamin

Contender Video are offering 40 Animals and Music Fun videos. The latest Jamboree video is jam-packed with no less than eight of your favourite episodes featuring Floella Benjamin, the Bopkins, Mimi the monkey, and Scruff the dog.

If you'd like the chance to win one, just answer the following question correctly. . .

HOW TO ENTER
What's the name of the monkey in Jamboree?
(You'll find the answer on this page).

Write the answer on a postcard or sealed empty envelope. Add your name, address, and age, and post it before the closing date of 27 January 2001 to:-

Jamboree Comp, CiTV Annual, Egmont World Ltd, Deanway Technology Centre, Wilmslow Rd., Handforth, Cheshire, SK9 3FB.

The first 40 Telly Tots names picked from the Bopkins' cupboard, will each receive a Jamboree video, as shown. Good luck!

Rules:-
40 winners will be chosen at random and notified by post. Judges decision will be final.
No correspondence will be entered into. The winners' names will be made available from Egmont World Limited (on request) after 5 February 2001. Please enclose a stamped addressed envelope. Employees (and their relatives) of Egmont World Limited and their associated companies are not eligible to enter. Entries are limited to one per person. Competition is open to residents of the UK, Channel Isles and Ireland. The Publishers reserve the right to vary prizes, subject to availability. Closing date for entries is 27 January 2001.

40

Sweep Makes a cake

1. Sooty had been cleaning the windows of Sooty Heights Hotel. This gave him peace and quiet to think up new ideas.

2. Lots of guests were staying in the hotel. Sooty thought it would be a good idea to put on a Magic Show to entertain them.

3. "A Magic Show is a very good idea," said Sweep. "I can make something special for everyone to eat as well."

4. "Yum, yum," said Scampi. "That sounds good. What are you going to make, Sweep?" he asked.

5 "This morning I dug up a bone THIS big from the garden," said Sweep proudly. "There should be enough to feed the guests."

6 "Don't be so silly, Sweep," said Liana. "You can't give the guests at Sooty Heights an old bone to eat!"

7 Sooty thought that was very funny. "I think they would rather eat a nice cake than a bone," he chuckled.

8 So Sweep went to the kitchen to make cakes instead. "You're making an awful mess there, Sweep," said Soo.

9

"Would you like me to help you?" asked Soo. "Yes please," said Sweep. "Good. Just do as I say," said Soo.

10

"Stirring cake mix makes my arms tired," said Sweep. "Okay," said Soo. "Put it somewhere safe and have a rest."

11

Sweep looked around for somewhere to put the cake mixture. "I think it will be safe here," he thought.

12

Soon, it was time for the Magic Show to start. Sooty and Sweep introduced the show, dressed up as clowns.

13

Richard began with a card trick. "Why don't you wear the top hat," whispered Sooty. "You'll look more like a real magician."

14

Oh no! Sweep had put the cake mix in the hat! "Yuk! I'm covered," spluttered poor Richard. The guests all laughed and clapped.

15

"Oops, sorry," muttered Sweep. "Never mind," said Sooty. "The audience thought that was the best part of the act!"

the end

WHAT CAN YOU REMEMBER?

1 Who had the idea to put on a Magic Show?

2 Who offered to help Sweep make the cake?

3 Where did Sweep put the cake mix?

4 Who got covered in cake mix?

Answers: 1: Sooty 2: Soo 3: In the top hat 4: Richard

Teddybears

Coloured in

Louise   Robert   Sara   William

by ....

Helping out

1

"What a horrible rainy day," said Annie. "Yuk! my fur's getting soaking wet," replied Teddy, as the toys ran for shelter.

2

"Quickly, Teddy," shouted Annie. "We can shelter under the boxes in this market stall."

3

Teddy jumped into a box, but he wasn't happy with what he found inside. "Sprouts!" he said. "I hate sprouts!"

4

"Let's take cover in this house instead," suggested Teddy. "As long as the people who live there don't see us," said Annie.

Annie and Teddy are two lost toys trying to find their way back home.

5

"We'll just wait here until it stops raining," said Annie. Teddy peeked inside a room. "We're not alone," he whispered.

6

"What are you doing here?" said an angry toy elephant. "Clear off," said the toy monkey. "This is our house, not yours!"

7

"Don't be cross," said Annie. "We're only sheltering from the rain." But the other toys didn't believe her.

8

The elephant used his trunk to shove Annie outside. "You're not taking our place in this house," he bellowed.

9

"Hold on a minute," said Teddy. "We don't want to take your place! Whatever gave you that idea?"

10

"We're all getting rather old and tatty," Elephant replied, "and we were worried our owner might throw us out."

11

"Gosh! We can't allow that, Elephant," said Annie. "Perhaps I should try to smarten you all up."

12

Annie found a needle and thread and set about mending the tatty old toys. "There," she said, "now you look as good as new."

Later, the little boy who lived in the house came home from school. He was delighted to see how smart his toys looked.

"I love my toys," he said, "and I'll never, ever, throw you away." The toys were very pleased to hear that.

"That's our good deed for the day," said Teddy. "Now it's time to move on and find our home," said Annie.

the end

WHAT CAN YOU REMEMBER?

1 Why did Annie and Teddy find shelter?

2 What did Teddy find in the box under the stall?

3 What colour are the brussel sprouts?

4 Who mended the toys?

Answers: 1: It was raining, 2: Brussel sprouts, 3: Green, 4: Annie.

The doctors and nurses of Hilltop Hospital are always very busy. They have lots of people to look after.

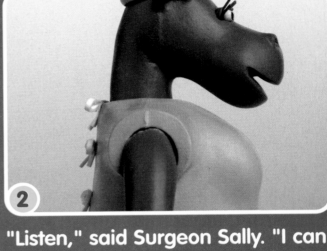

"Listen," said Surgeon Sally. "I can hear the ambulance siren." That means a new patient is arriving at the hospital.

The ambulance drivers are the Two Teds. They make sure that people who are not feeling well can get to the hospital quickly.

"A new patient for you," said Ted One. "It's an elephant with a sprained trunk." "Bring her in," said Surgeon Sally.

sy, busy

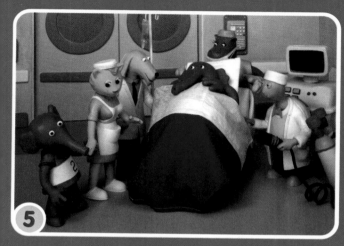

5

"Don't worry, Elephant," said kind Doctor Matthews. "You will soon be feeling much better."

6

"With the help of Doctor Atticus, Surgeon Sally, and Nurse Kitty, you'll be well in no time," he said.

7

"I'll leave Elephant in your safe hands, now Nurse," said Doctor Matthews. "I've lots of other patients to see."

8

The patients at Hilltop Hospital were there for all sorts of different reasons. Some of them had come especially to have babies.

9

One of the patients was a giraffe with a sore neck. His friend had brought him a scarf to keep his neck warm.

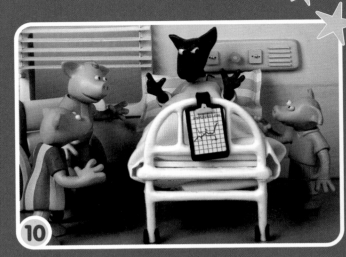

10

All of the patients looked forward to visiting time. That's when their friends and family arrived to help cheer them up.

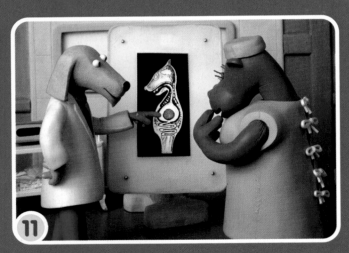

11

The x-ray machine took special photos of patients. This was so the doctors could see inside people's bodies to find out what was wrong.

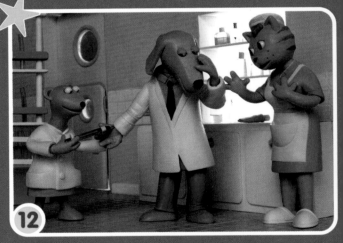

12

All of the staff at Hilltop Hospital worked so hard to help people. "It's been a long day," said Doctor Matthews.

13

"You look very tired too, Doctor Atticus," said Doctor Matthews. "I always look like this," laughed Doctor Atticus.

14

"There's another call coming in," said Ted One. "Another patient for us to collect and take to hospital."

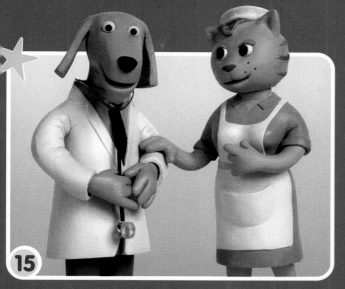

15

"There's always someone new to help," said Nurse Kitty. "That's what we do best at Hilltop Hospital," smiled the Doctor.

the end

WHAT CAN YOU REMEMBER?

1 Who drives the ambulance?

2 What is wrong with the elephant?

3 Who can visit people in hospital?

4 What is the nurse called?

Answers: **1: The Two Teds 2:** She had a sprained trunk.
3: Family and friends. 4: Nurse Kitty.

Fancy dress

"What shall we do later on today?" asked Robert, as the Teddybears were sitting around the table eating their breakfast. William knew what he wanted to do. "I'm going to eat all of my breakfast," he said, biting into a sausage. William loved to eat!

Robert, looking at the other Teddybears. Charles stroked his chin. "That's a good point, Robert," said Charles. "We should do something different."

"Yes," agreed Sara, "Let's do something special. Does anyone have any ideas?" Louise had a suggestion. "Let's have a Fancy Dress Party!" she said. "We can each make different outfits to dress up in!"

Charles
Sara
William
Robert
Louise

"I mean what are we going to do after breakfast?" asked

The other Teddybears liked Louise's idea. "That's brilliant," said Robert, getting excited. "What shall we wear?"

Party Teddybears

Charles smiled at Robert. "That's the whole point of Fancy Dress," he said. "We don't tell anyone which outfit we're making. Then it's a big surprise when we arrive at the party!"

"I don't know what I'll dress up as," said William, "but I know it's going to be good."

Louise giggled. "William loves his food so much that I bet he'll dress up as a giant sausage," she said, teasing the red bear.

Infact, none of the Teddybears had decided what to wear yet, but they had to come up with ideas soon.

"Perhaps the fresh air will help us think," said Sara. "Let's go in the garden." Sara loved to watch the birds and insects going about their business.

"Me too," said Sara. "So let's get to work making our outfits - in secret, though! Remember, we won't show each other our costumes until the party."

"Look! There's a pretty little Ladybird," said Sara.

Just then, Louise jumped up, "I've just had an idea of what my Fancy Dress will be!" She giggled. "I'm going to get to work making my costume right away," and she ran into the house.

"I've had an idea as well," said William. "Yes, I've suddenly had a thought too," said Charles. "So have I," said Robert.

Later that day, it was time for the Fancy Dress to begin. Louise had decorated the house with lots of colourful balloons, and William had made a nice chocolate cake for everyone.

Then they all put on their Fancy Dress costumes, and what a surprise they had! Apart from Louise, they were all dressed up as insects!

What a funny sight the other Teddybears looked. Sara laughed. "We must have all had the same idea when I

spoke about the insects in the garden," she said.

"Never mind," said Charles. "We can still enjoy the party." William licked his lips. "Yes," he said, "especially the chocolate cake!"

the end

subscriptions to win CiTV Telly Tots

We've got 25 CiTV Telly Tots Magazine subscriptions to give away for a whole year! Plus, a very special Dream Street Playset will also be sent to the first winning entry.

HOW TO ENTER

For a chance to win, list the CiTV characters shown in this Annual. Put them in order of the ones you like best (with your favourites at the top).

Featuring your favourite friends from Dream Street in one fun-filled playset (all that's required are batteries).

Write your list on a postcard or the back of a sealed envelope (include your name, address and age), and post to:

CiTV Subs Competition, CiTV Annual, Egmont World Ltd, Deanway Technology Centre, Wilmslow Rd., Handforth, Cheshire, SK9 3FB.
(Entries to arrive before 27 January 2001).

Rules:-
25 lucky winners will be chosen at random and notified by post. The Judges' decision will be final. No correspondence will be entered into. The winners' names will be made available from Egmont World Ltd (on request) after 5 February 2001. Please enclose a stamped addressed envelope. Employees (and their relatives) of Egmont World Ltd., and their associated companies are not eligible to enter. Entries are limited to one per person. Competition is open to residents of the UK, Channel Isles and Ireland. The Publishers reserve the right to vary prizes, subject to availability. Closing date for entries is 27 January 2001.